W9-CTU-873

THE CIRCLE GAME

JONI MITCHELL

Series Editor • Glen Downey
Art • Nataly Kim

In creating the graphic poetry in this collection, we made many choices interpreting the poet's original language and ideas. Our hope is that these graphic poems will get you to see poetry — literally and figuratively — in a whole new way!

SCHOLASTIC

175 Hillmount Road
Markham, Ontario
L6C 1Z7

A Rubicon book published in association with Scholastic Canada

Ru bicon © 2009 Rubicon Publishing Inc.

Editorial Director: Amy Land
Project Manager/Editor: Christine Boocock
Creative Director: Jennifer Drew
Art Director: Rebecca Buchanan
Graphic Designer: Andrea Jankun

The publisher gratefully acknowledges the following for permission to reprint copyrighted material in this book.

Every reasonable effort has been made to trace the owners of copyrighted material and to make due acknowledgement. Any errors or omissions drawn to our attention will be gladly rectified in future editions.

"The Circle Game" Words and Music by JONI MITCHELL © 1966 (Renewed) CRAZY CROW MUSIC. All Rights Administered by SONY/ATV MUSIC PUBLISHING. 8 Music Square West, Nashville, TN 37203. All Rights Reserved. Used by Permission of ALFRED PUBLISHING CO., INC.

9 10 11 12 13   5 4 3 2 1

ISBN 10: 1-55448-736-6
ISBN 13: 978-1-55448-736-3

THE CIRCLE GAME continues to be a song treasured by many people, even though it was released more than four decades ago. Perhaps one of the reasons is that it deals with a subject that interests us all — growing up.

In this poem, Joni Mitchell explores four stages in the life of a young man. Without focusing on the good or the bad aspects of life, Mitchell presents an honest portrait of one person moving away from childhood.

Using the carousel as a symbol, Mitchell shows how life goes around and around, filled with ups and downs. The poem highlights the importance of living life to its fullest by truly appreciating every moment as well as the people in our lives.

In this graphic version of "The Circle Game," artist Nataly Kim depicts in her sensitive illustrations the different hopes, fears, and dreams that are part of each stage of our lives.

Yesterday a child came out to wonder

Caught a dragonfly inside a jar

Fearful

when the sky was full of thunder

And tearful

at the falling of a star

Then the child moved ten times round the seasons

Skated over ten clear
frozen streams

And the seasons they go round and round
And the painted ponies go up and down

We're captive on the carousel of time

We can't return we can only look

Behind from where we came

And go round and round and round

In the circle game

Sixteen springs and sixteen summers

gone now

Cartwheels turn to car wheels
thru the town

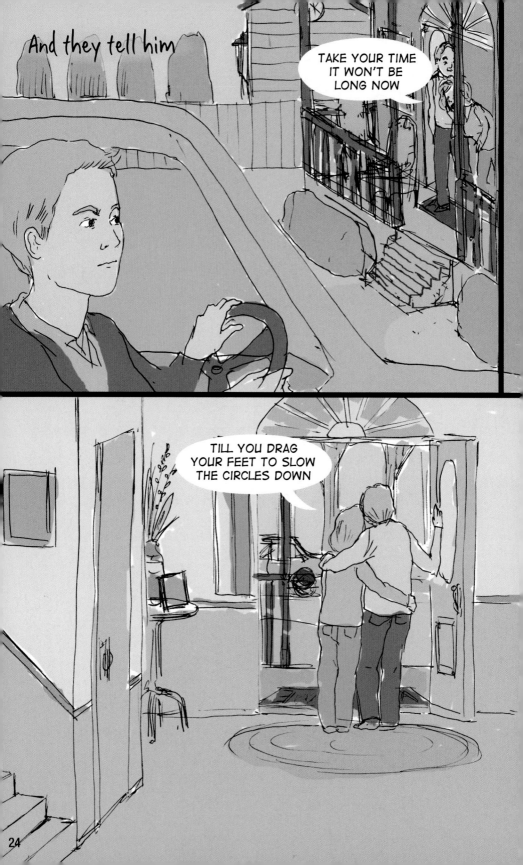

And the seasons they go round and round

And the painted ponies go up and down
We're captive on the carousel of time

We can't return
we can only look
Behind from where
we came

So the years spin by

and now the boy is twenty

though his dreams have lost some grandeur coming true

There'll be new dreams

maybe better dreams and plenty

Before the last revolving year is through

And the seasons they go round and round

And the painted ponies go up and down

We're captive on the carousel of time

We can't return we can only look
Behind from where we came

In the circle game

THE CIRCLE GAME

Joni Mitchell

Yesterday a child came out to wonder
Caught a dragonfly inside a jar
Fearful when the sky was full of thunder
And tearful at the falling of a star

5 Then the child moved ten times round the seasons
Skated over ten clear frozen streams
Words like when you're older must appease him
And promises of someday make his dreams

And the seasons they go round and round
10 And the painted ponies go up and down
We're captive on the carousel of time
We can't return we can only look
Behind from where we came
And go round and round and round
15 In the circle game

Sixteen springs and sixteen summers gone now
Cartwheels turn to car wheels thru the town
And they tell him take your time it won't be long now
Till you drag your feet to slow the circles down

²⁰ And the seasons they go round and round
And the painted ponies go up and down
We're captive on the carousel of time
We can't return we can only look
Behind from where we came
²⁵ And go round and round and round
In the circle game

So the years spin by and now the boy is twenty
Though his dreams have lost some grandeur coming true
There'll be new dreams maybe better dreams and plenty
³⁰ Before the last revolving year is through

And the seasons they go round and round
And the painted ponies go up and down
We're captive on the carousel of time
We can't return we can only look
35 Behind from where we came
And go round and round and round
In the circle game

BETWEEN THE LINES

THE CIRCLE GAME

We don't often think of poetry when we listen to our favourite singer on the radio, but if you think about it, songs are really poetry set to music. Songwriters compose in lines and verses, not sentences and paragraphs.

What makes **song lyrics** a bit different from the poems we usually read in school is the chorus. This is part of the lyrics that is repeated a number of times throughout the song, usually after each verse.

In some ways, this repetition allows us to enjoy the most important, interesting, and meaningful part of the song again and again. It is also typically set to a melody that is different from the other verses in the song. Here is the chorus in Joni Mitchell's "The Circle Game":

And the seasons they go round and round
And the painted ponies go up and down
We're captive on the carousel of time
We can't return we can only look
Behind from where we came
And go round and round and round
In the circle game

Though written to accompany music in a song, Mitchell's use of repetition, rhyme, and imagery gives these lyrics a poetic feel. She uses the image of a carousel to represent years of life passing.

Each of the verses of Mitchell's song tells us about what is happening to the boy at a particular age, but the chorus sums up the song's powerful message: that we can't return to the past, we can only think about it and cherish it.

FYI

It is believed that "The Circle Game" was inspired by the Neil Young song "Sugar Mountain." Young wrote this song when he was 19 years old. It is about growing up and about the sadness of leaving childhood behind. Mitchell's song, however, is more positive. Childhood can be carefree and fun, but as grown-ups, people often have some of the greatest experiences of their lives.

- Find a recording of "The Circle Game" and listen to it. Which do you prefer — the audio version or this graphic version? Why? Think of something you would use as a symbol for the cycle of life. Write a four-line chorus or a rap around this symbol. Share it with a partner.

- Choose a favourite song of yours and find the lyrics for it. Do you think that the lyrics read like poetry? Why or why not?

I need to explore and discover, and so that has given me... what seems like courage but really it's just in my stars, there's nothing I can do about it.

— Joni Mitchell

Born Roberta Joan Anderson, Joni Mitchell (b. 1943) is a Canadian songwriter, musician, and visual artist. She started out singing on the streets of Toronto and in Western Canada before becoming part of the folk music scene of the 1960s. It was then that her career took off with a series of incredible songs, such as "Big Yellow Taxi," "Both Sides Now," and, of course, "The Circle Game."

Mitchell is known for her amazing songwriting abilities. Music critic Martha Bayles once wrote in the *New York Times* that Mitchell's best songs "combine complex melodies, eloquent lyrics, and strong passions tempered by intelligence."

tempered: *counterbalanced; softened*

Throughout her remarkable career, Mitchell's music has influenced a wide range of artists, including Madonna, Elvis Costello, and Prince. Mitchell has also received a great deal of recognition. In 1981, she was inducted into the Canadian Music Hall of Fame by Prime Minister Pierre Trudeau, who called her a "Canadian who makes us proud to be Canadian." In 1997, she was the first Canadian woman to be inducted into the Rock and Roll Hall of Fame. She has also won several Grammy Awards, including the Lifetime Achievement Award in 2002.

Joni Mitchell

INDEX

Photo Credits